The Godly Man

Personal Bible Studies
for the
Christian Man

Gene Warr

Forewo... ...Charlie Riggs

Creative Resources

Waco, Texas

Workbook
THE GODLY MAN

Acknowledgements

My Special Thanks

—To my wife, Irma, who patiently kept telling me that it could be done and whose personal touch can be seen on every page.

—To my secretary, Marty Townsend, for her grace to endure.

—To the men in my Bible Study group who went through the study and have contributed so much in research, suggestions, and prayers.

—To Lorne Sanny and Charlie Riggs, without whose encouragement, faithfulness, prayers, and continuing investment in my life I would have had nothing to write.

—To my memory of my father whose example and principles of life so shaped my own.

Contents

The Godly Man as a Husband

The Godly Man as a Father

Foreword

Today, perhaps more than at any time in history, multitudes are involved in personal Bible study and prayer, individually and with fellowship groups. A tremendous spiritual hunger is being met by a variety of good study materials that are currently available.

Personally, I believe that *The Godly Man: Personal Bible Studies for the Christian Man* is unique. In this book, you have an excellent combination of well-designed lessons with relevance to the issues and problems of the day, deeply rooted in Scripture with practical application of biblical truth to specific areas of life. You also have a large variety of rich resource material in the "Suggestions for Further Study" section at the end of each session.

If you use this study in a group setting, another unique feature you have is a "built-in" fellowship through prayer and sharing. Group members pray for each other daily, and in weekly Bible discussion share their Bible discoveries and what God is doing in their lives.

I am confident that any person who is willing to follow the disciplines set forth in these studies will greatly enhance his relationship to God and man and his effectiveness as a Christian witness.

Charlie Riggs
Counselor Training and Followup
The Billy Graham Evangelistic
Association

About *The Godly Man* Bible Study

Purpose

To help produce in you the kind of person whose life is explainable only in terms of God. To create in you the kind of life other men seek for help and counsel. To enable you to more perfectly reflect the Lord Jesus Christ in his glory.

Design

The Godly Man Bible Study is designed for individual or group use.

1. This book, *The Godly Man: Personal Bible Studies for the Christian Man,* contains twenty-two sessions you can work through at your own pace and in the privacy of your personal study time. It is meant to be written in. You would need no further materials unless you desired to do the additional study recommended at the close of each session.

2. This workbook is also part of a complete program for groups utilizing a Teacher's Guide and four 90-minute cassette tapes. It is designed to be covered in twenty-two, 1 hour sessions and contains everything you would need to conduct an effective group study.

Suggestions for Further Study

At the end of each chapter you will find "Suggestions for Further Study." The books and pamphlets may be obtained from your local Christian bookstore. The tapes are available on a free loan basis from:

> The Foundation Library
> 435 West Boyd
> Norman, Oklahoma 73069

Follow-Up

The Godly Man Bible Study is the companion program for *The Godly Woman* course. Both are available with *Personal Bible Studies* workbooks for individual study and a Leader's kit for group use. For information concerning these and over fifty additional group study programs available through Creative Resources, write P.O. Box 1790, Waco, Texas 76703 or call toll free 1–800–433–2380. A no-obligation thirty-day review program is available upon request.

THE GODLY MAN AS A DISCIPLE

CHAPTER I
THE FOUNDATION OF A DISCIPLE

The Foundation of a Disciple.
"For other foundation can no man lay than that is laid, which is
Jesus Christ." I Cor. 3:11

I. Who Jesus Christ is:
  A. He is God.
    1. Jesus Claimed:
      a. Matthew 28:18

. . . .
. . . .

      b. Matthew 9:6

. . . .
. . . .

      c. John 14:9

. . . .
. . . .

      d. John 10:30

. . . .
. . . .

      e. John 15:21

. . . .
. . . .

      f. John 10:10

. . . .
. . . .

    2. The Bible says He:
      a. John 8:58, Col. 1:17

. . . .
. . . .

      b. Col. 1:16

. . . .
. . . .

B. He is a perfect man.
   3. Match the following human characteristics of Jesus with the verses:

   weary _____   John 4:6
   hungry _____   Matt. 4:2
   sleepy _____   Mark 4:38
   sorrowful _____   John 11:35
   tempted _____   Heb. 4:15

II What Jesus did.
   4. Why did He come? Luke 19:10

   . . . .

   . . . .
   5. Romans 5:8 says that God showed His love for us by

   . . . .

   . . . .
   6. Who needs Jesus to die for him? . . . .
   Why is this true? Express Romans 6:23 in your own words . . . .

   . . . .
   7. What did Christ do on the cross? I Peter 2:24 . . . .

   . . . .
   8. What sign did Jesus say He would give the Jews? John 2:18-22 . . . .

   . . . .

   9. What sign did Jesus give? Luke 24:1-7 . . . .

   . . . .

   . . . .

"God is on one side and all the people on the other side, and Christ Jesus, Himself man, is between them to bring them together."
I Timothy 2:5 Living Bible

III. What the life, death, and resurrection of Jesus means.

10. Man is separated from God by sin. According to Jesus Christ, what ways are available to man by which he may return to God? John 14:6

. . . .

. . . .

. . . .

. . . .

11. Who does God want in fellowship with Himself? I Tim. 2:4, II Peter 3:9. . . . .

. . . .

12. Why are some people still not in fellowship with God? John 3:18 . . . .

. . . .

. . . .

13. What is the condition of those who have not believed Jesus? John 3:36 . . . .

. . . .

. . . .

14. When a person realizes that he is separated from God because of his sin, what should his response be? Luke 13:3 . . . .

. . . .

. . . .

". . . Except ye repent, ye shall all likewise perish." Luke 13:3

15. What does it mean to repent? Matt. 3:2-8 . . . .

. . . .

. . . .

. . . .

16. According to I John 5:11, 12, who has eternal life? (fellowship with God) . . . .

. . . .

17. In the light of John 1:12, 13, and Eph. 2:8, 9, those who have eternal life (fellowship with God) and will be in heaven, are those who:

True	False	
( )	( )	Do more good things than bad during their lifetime.
( )	( )	Repent of their sins.
( )	( )	Live as good as some church members.
( )	( )	Clean up their lives so as to be acceptable with God.
( )	( )	Receive Jesus Christ.
( )	( )	Join a church and are baptized.
( )	( )	Are sincere.
( )	( )	Really believe in something.

18. In your opinion, what must one do in order to be in fellowship with God and have eternal life? . . . .

. . . .
. . . .
. . . .
. . . .
. . . .

19. Do you have eternal life? . . . .
20. How do you know? (125 words or less) . . . .

. . . .
. . . .
. . . .
. . . .
. . . .
. . . .
. . . .
. . . .
. . . .

Suggestions For Further Study
Tape No. BSU 77a — "Discipleship"

CHAPTER II

GOD'S PROVISION FOR A DISCIPLE

I. The source of God's provision is His grace. Grace has been defined as "the unmerited favor of God." Or, as

<u>G</u>od's
<u>R</u>iches
<u>A</u>t
<u>C</u>hrist's
<u>E</u>xpense

Grace is God doing for us what we in no way deserve. Mercy is God not doing to us what we so richly deserve.

1. Why did Paul say he was the man he was? I Cor. 15:10

   ....

2. To whom will God be gracious? Exodus 33:19 ....

   ....

3. Why did God choose Israel as His special people? Deut. 7:7-8 ....

   ....

4. If we try to earn God's favor in any way, what does this do to His grace? Gal. 2:21 ....

   ....

II. The channel of grace.

5. How do we receive the grace of God? John 1:17 ....

   ....

   ....

6. According to Romans 3:24, we are justified (declared "not guilty" and made right with God) by .... , through ....

   ....

7. What is another result of the grace of God? Eph. 2:7

   ....

8. Eph. 2:8 teaches us that we are saved through .... and that it is the .... of God.

—7—

9. The grace of God comes to those who believe through Jesus Christ. According to the following scriptures, what good things come to us through Jesus Christ?

Col. 2:9-10 ....

....

Eph. 1:3 ....

....

1 Cor. 1:30 ....

....

....

I Cor. 1:4-5 ....

Phil. 4:13 ....

III. The means of grace.
   10. Our access to the grace of God as given through Jesus Christ is by .... Romans 5:1-2.
   11. What are the three time elements in regard to our faith? II Cor. 1:10 ....

....

Romans 5:9-10 teaches that we have been saved from the penalty of sin (past), are being delivered from the power of sin (present) and will ultimately be freed from the presence of sin (future). Past FAITH is that which we exercised when we received Jesus Christ. Future FAITH is the looking forward to being with Him in heaven. Present FAITH is believing and trusting Him for each day's problems now.

   12. Col. 2:6 says we should walk in the same way we received Christ. We received Him (became children of God) by ....

....

(Gal. 3:26)

....

(Rom. 1:17)

....

Col. 2:6 in the Living Bible says "and now just as you trusted Christ to save you, trust Him, too, for each day's problems; live in vital union with Him."

13. Self effort is the opposite of faith. What area of your life are you still trying to handle by your own effort and worry, instead of trusting Jesus Christ? . . . .

. . . .

. . . .

14. What will you do this coming week to bring faith into operation in this area, so that you may experience the grace of God? (Express it in personal terms using the pronoun me, my, and mine) . . . .

. . . .

. . . .

IV. The results of grace.

15. What is God's will for every born-again believer?
Romans 8:29 . . . .

. . . .

Eph. 4:13 . . . .

. . . .

16. What are we commanded to do? . . . . .
II Peter 3:18 . . . .

. . . .

. . . .

Much of the balance of this study booklet will deal with the "how to" of growing in the grace and knowledge of Jesus and becoming more and more like Him. You are embarking on the world's most exciting adventure.

17. As we grow in discipleship, certain things will begin to be true of our lives. List some of them:
John 13:34-35 . . . .

. . . .

John 8:31 . . . .

. . . .

John 15:8 . . . .

. . . .

Acts 6:7 . . . .

18. Which of these areas do you feel you need the most help in at this time? . . . .

. . . .

19. What will you do this next week to allow God to minister His grace to you in this area? (Be specific — don't deal in generalities) . . . .

. . . .

. . . .

. . . .

Suggestions For Further Study

Tape 1272 A, B — "Grace of God"

The Attributes of God by Arthur W. Pink, Reiner Publications.

The Saving Life of Christ by Major W. Ian Thomas, Zondervan Publishing House.

CHAPTER III

THE CHRIST-CENTERED LIFE
[THE WHEEL]

(Used by permission of The Navigators)

The key to living a victorious, Spirit-filled Christian life is Jesus Christ as the Center and Lord of all we do. With Christ in control, life is balanced and effective. The Wheel illustrates this Christ-centered life.

WHEEL EXPLANATION

- Just as the driving force in a wheel comes from the hub; so the power to live the Christian life comes from Jesus Christ the Center. He lives in us in the Person of the Holy Spirit, whose expressed purpose is to glorify Christ. The rim represents the Christian responding to Christ's Lordship through whole-hearted, day-by-day obedience to Him.

- The spokes show the means by which Christ's power becomes operative in our lives. We maintain personal contact with God through the vertical spokes — the Word and prayer. The Word is our spiritual food as well as our sword for spiritual battle. It is the foundational spoke for effective Christian living.

- Opposite this is the spoke representing Prayer. Through prayer we have direct communication with our heavenly Father and receive provision for our needs. As we pray we show our dependence upon and trust in Him.

- The horizontal spokes concern our relationship to people — believers, through Christian fellowship; and unbelievers, through witnessing. Fellowship centered around the Lord Jesus Christ provides the mutual encouragement, admonition and stimulation we all need.

- The first three spokes prepare us for passing on to others all that we have received from the Lord. This is accomplished through Witnessing, sharing our own experience of Christ and declaring and explaining the Gospel, God's power to save.

PART 1 — THE HUB AND THE RIM

I. Christ the Hub.
  1. Why should Christ be the center of the believer's life?
     John 13:13 . . . .
     I Cor. 7:23 . . . .
     Heb. 13:8 . . . .
     I Peter 5:7 . . . .
  2. In your opinion, what are some of the substitutions
     people make for Christ in the center of their lives? . . . . .
     . . . .
     . . . .
     . . . .
     . . . .

II. The Rim.
  1. How will others judge our relationship to Jesus Christ?
     Matt. 7:15-20. . . . .
     . . . .
     . . . .
  2. Our obedience indicates:
     John 14:15 . . . .
     John 15:14 . . . .
     Matt. 7:21 . . . .
     I John 2:3-5 . . . .
  3. What are some things God promises those who obey
     Him?
     Deut. 28:2 . . . .
     Ex. 19:5 . . . .
     I Peter 1:22 . . . .
  4. What are we to obey? John 14:21, Joshua 22:5 . . . .
     . . . .
  5. What are the two greatest commandments? Luke 10:27
     . . . .
     . . . .

6. I Sam. 15:22 teaches us that obedience is better than .. .. There is no substitute for obedience in the Christian life.

7. List three "sacrifices" that people try to substitute for obedience today: ....

8. Express Romans 8:32 in your own words. ....

9. In the light of Romans 8:32
   A. What has God given us? ....
   B. What will He give us? ....

10. Why does God want us to obey Him? Jeremiah 29:11 .. ..

Ephesians 1:8 in the Living Bible says "And He has showered down upon us the riches of His grace—for how well he understands us and knows what is best for us at all times."

11. Do you believe God knows what is best for you and wants the best for you? ....

12. Then why would you not obey Him? ....

13. Obedience is a matter of the .... Deut. 5:29

PART 2 — THE VERTICAL INTAKE SPOKES

III. The Word.

   1. Why do you believe what you believe? Or, asking it another way, what is the basis of your final authority for what you believe?

(Check One)

    A.   It seems reasonable to me.
    B.   I feel that way about it.
    C.   My own experience.
    D.   The experience of others.
    E.   My church tells me.
    F.   My parents taught me.
    G.   The Bible.
    H.   The sacred writings of the ages.

WHERE IS THE BLUEPRINT

   2. In II Tim. 3:16, what does the Bible say about
    A. It's origin? ....
    ....

    B. It's profit in:
      1) .... (what to believe and do)
      2) .... (when we get off the road)
      3) .... (how to get back on the road)
      4) .... (how to stay on the road)

   3. List opposite the scriptures below some further claims of the Bible:

      II Tim. 3:15 ....
      I Peter 2:2 ....
      Ps. 119:105 ....
      John 15:3 ....
      Ps. 119:165 ....
      Romans 10:17 ....

BIBLE

The Word of God is MATCHLESS — Man cannot duplicate it.

The Word of God is ULTIMATE — it is final, it will not be changed, there is no appeal, John 12:48.

The Word of God is PERFECT — how would you improve on John 3:16?

The Word of God is TIMELESS — The Bible works now and forever.

The Word of God is INDESTRUCTABLE — Man cannot destroy it. Luke 21:33.

Whenever the Word of God is ineffective in a life, it is for one of three reasons:
1. Neglect
2. Doubt
3. Disobedience

IV. Prayer.
1. Define prayer . . . .
2. What are two reasons why we miss much of what God has for us?
   A. James 4:2 . . . .

   . . . .
   B. James 4:3 . . . .

   . . . .
3. Prayer is an act of faith. How should we pray?
   Matthew 21:22 . . . .
4. Since God knows our needs (Matt. 6:8), why should we bring them before Him?
   (MATCH THE PHRASES WITH THE VERSES)

   Luke 18:1   (   )   1. So our joy might be complete
   John 16:24 (   )   2. It is commanded.
   Ps. 62:8   (   )   3. To experience His peace.
   Phil. 4:6, 7 (   )   4. To demonstrate trust in Him
5. What do you feel Matthew 7:7 teaches about prayer?

   . . . .

   . . . .

   . . . .
6. Our God is a God of law and order. The physical laws operate in certain ways. Effects obey causes. This is true spiritually. God has placed some conditions on effective prayer. Discover and list some of them below.

   Isa. 59:1, 2 . . . .

   . . . .
   I John 3:22 . . . .

   . . . .
   I John 5:14, 15 . . . .

   . . . .
   I Peter 3:7 . . . .

7. How can we know when we are praying "according to God's will?" ....
....
....

8. What does it mean to pray "In Jesus Name?" ....
....

9. How can we prevent sin from hindering our prayer life? I John 1:9 ....
....

10. Most people have experienced the discouragement of seemingly unanswered prayers. Match up some reasons for ineffective prayer with the verses below:

Job 35:12, 13   ( )   1. Lack of heart preparation
Eph. 6:12   ( )   2. Pride
Ps. 139:23, 24   ( )   3. Satan's hindering
Matt. 6:33   ( )   4. Poor value system
Mark 11:25, 26   ( )   5. Lack of faith
James 1:6-8   ( )   6. Unforgiving spirit

11. We have discovered some conditions of effective prayer and some hindrances. Which two do you feel you fail in most? ....

Why? ....
....
....
....
....
....

12. What will you do this week to allow God to begin correcting these in your life? (Who will you ask to check up on you next week?) ....

. . . .
. . . .
. . . .
. . . .
. . . .
. . . .
. . . .

Suggestions For Further Study

Prayer, by O'Hallesby, Augsburg Press
The Prayer Life by Andrew Murray, Moody Press
How to Pray by R. A. Torrey, Moody Press
Prevailing Prayer by D. L. Moody, Moody Press

Tape 368 — "Prayer"
Tape 1246 —"Immediate Asking and Receiving"
Tape 60 — "Authority and Sufficiency of the Scriptures"
Tape 87 — "The Word of God"

PART 3 — THE HORIZONTAL OUTREACH SPOKES

V. Fellowship: Fellowship is defined as comradeship, companionship, a relation in which parties hold something in common, mutual sharing, or friendly association. Someone has said, in the Christian context, that fellowship is two fellows on the same ship going in the same direction.

1. What is the basis of Christian fellowship? I John 1:3 . . .
. . . .
. . . .

2. The fellowship of the world rests on many different bases. Name some of the things which draw people together.

. . . .
. . . .
. . . .
. . . .
. . . .

3. Why is Christian fellowship more permanent than the world's fellowship? Hebrews 13:8 . . . .
. . . .

4. Discover and list from Acts 2:42 four things in which the early church continued.

. . . .

5. The New English Bible translates the part of Acts 2:42 on fellowship as "sharing the common life." Explain in practical ways what the term "sharing the common life" means to you. . . . .
. . . .
. . . .
. . . .

6. Why is fellowship important to us?

Matthew 18:19-20 ....

Lev. 26:8 ....

Ecc. 4:9, 10 ....

Heb. 10:25 ....

7. Check two basic things which you feel hinder Christian fellowship most today:

Pride   ( )
Selfishness   ( )
Lack of Love   ( )
Lack of understanding ( )
Independence   ( )
Busyness   ( )
Fear   ( )
Hyprocrisy   ( )
Sin in the life   ( )
Other ....( )

8. Do you have at least one Christian friend with whom you are able to be completely yourself, knowing he will accept you and love you anyway?

A. If so, pause now and thank God for him. Thank him for being this kind of friend this coming week.

B. If not, pause now and ask God to bring someone like this into your life.

Read the prayer of Jesus in John 17 with the intention of discovering what He revealed about the importance of fellowship.

VI. Witness

1. Whose job is it to save people? I Tim. 1:15 ....

2. We are simply the .... of Christ. II Cor. 5:19, 20

3. The power is in (Romans 1:16. Check one)
The presentation   ( )
The one presenting Christ   ( )
Just the right setting   ( )
The Gospel   ( )

4. Define "the Gospel" in your own words. I Cor. 15:3, 4 ..

....

....

....

5. What is a personal testimony? I John 1:3, Acts 4:20 . . .

. . . .

. . . .

. . . .

. . . .

. . . .

. . . .

6. Read Acts 26:4-23. This is Paul's personal testimony. From the following portions of Acts 26, match up the part of Paul's testimony which applies:

Acts 26:4-11 ( )   1. How Paul met Christ.

Acts 26:12-18 ( )   2. What life has been like since he met Christ.

Acts 26:19-23 ( )   3. What life was like before he met Christ.

7. Write out your own personal testimony in125 words or less, including the three basic elements mentioned above.

. . . .

. . . .

. . . .

. . . .

. . . .

. . . .

. . . .

. . . .

. . . .

. . . .

. . . .

. . . .

. . . .

. . . .

. . . .

. . . .

. . . .

. . . .

8. The "Do you know the steps to peace with God" pamphlet furnished with this study is one way of presenting the Gospel. Share the pamphlet completely with someone other than your family this week.

Suggestions For Further Study

Tape 1603 — "The Wheel"

Tape 1149 — "Enemies of Evangelism"

Tape 234 — "Witnessing"

Tape 772 — "Soul-Winning; Questions and Answers on Evangelism"

Tape 34 — "Harvest of Crops"

Tape BSU-170 — "Link In The Chain"

Winning Ways, by Leroy Eims, Victor Books.

Don't Fake It . . . Say it with Love, by Howard Hendricks, Victor Books

CHAPTER IV

THE DEVOTIONAL LIFE

The devotional life is known by many names. Daily devotions, morning watch, quiet time, time with the Lord. Naming it and knowing it doesn't mean we practice it. Few people do on a consistent basis. Whatever name is used, it means a specific time daily when we let God speak to us from His Word, the Bible, and when we speak to Him in prayer. It is daily, consistent fellowship with Christ.

I. Why daily devotions?
   Match the following statements with the appropriate scriptures answering the question, "why daily devotions?"

   ( ) Commanded by God   1. I Cor. 1:9
   ( ) God's Desire   2. II Cor. 3:18
   ( ) Worship   3. Ex. 34:2, 3
   ( ) Man's soul need   4. Jn. 4:24
   ( ) To know God   5. Jer. 2:32
   ( ) Part of God's call   6. Psa. 42:1, 2
   ( ) An invitation to us to   7. Isa. 43:10
        be like Christ

II. Examples of daily devotions in the lives of great men of the Bible.

   After the following scriptures, write down the name of a man and what he did or desired regarding his fellowship with God and in your opinion, why this was true.

   Gen. 19:27 . . . .
   . . . .
   . . . .

   Psa. 63:1, 2 . . . .
   . . . .
   . . . .

   Psa. 27:4 . . . .
   . . . .
   . . . .

   Ex. 33:14, 15 . . . .
   . . . .
   . . . .

Mark 1:35 . . . .
. . . .

Phil. 3:10 . . . .
. . . .

III Elements in the daily devotional life.
 A. Scriptures
  1. How was the king to read the scriptures according
   to Deut. 17:18-20? . . . .
   . . . .
  2. Why was he to read it? . . . .
   . . . .
  3. How does this apply to us today? . . . .
   . . . .
  4. Our identification with Christ is to be on a . . . .
   . . . . basis according to Luke 9:23.
 B. Prayer.
  1. When should we pray? Luke 18:1 . . . .
  2. What does I Thess. 5:17 mean? . . . .

  . . . .
  . . . .
  . . . .
  . . . .
  . . . .

  3. Effective prayer includes several elements. Match
   the elements with the scriptures then number them
   in the order that you feel they should be introduced
   in your own prayer time.
      ELEMENTS
   ( )   Praise . . . . Prov. 28:13
   ( )   Intercession . . . . Psa. 50:23
   ( )   Petition . . . . Eph. 5:20
   ( )   Confession . . . . I Sam. 12:23
   ( )   Thanksgiving . . . . Phil. 4:6-7

IV. Results of daily devotions.
 1. From the following scriptures, search and discover
  some results of a daily devotional life.

II Tim. 3:16 . . . .

. . . .

Joshua 1:8 . . . .

. . . .

. . . .
Hosea 6:6 (Living) "I don't want your sacrifices — I want your love; I don't want your offerings, — I want you to know Me." . . . .

. . . .

Psa. 139:23, 24 . . . .

. . . .

Psa. 119:105 . . . .

. . . .

I Peter 2:2, 3 . . . .

. . . .

I Jn. 1:7 . . . .

. . . .

. . . .

V. Hindrances to Daily Devotions.
  1. From the following scriptures, list some of the hindrances to an effective daily devotional life and decide how you would counteract each of them.

Hindrance	How I Would Counteract It.
Prov. 6:9	. . . .
. . . .	. . . .
. . . .	. . . .
Rev. 3:17	. . . .
. . . .	. . . .
. . . .	. . . .

Psa. 127:2 ....｜..

..............｜..

..............｜..

Matt. 6:33 ....｜..

..............｜..

..............｜..

Mark 4:19 ....｜..

..............｜..

..............｜..

I Jn. 2:15, 16 ......｜..

..............｜..

..............｜..

Psa. 66:18 ....｜..

..............｜..

....

Remember, in order to have an effective daily devotional life you need:

1. A time when you are at your best.
2. A place — quiet spot all alone.
3. A plan — some pre-determined approach.
4. A Bible — a translation you enjoy and don't mind writing in.
5. A notebook — to jot down what God says to you.
6. A prayer list — to help you remember.
7. An expectant heart — you have an audience with the King.

PRIVATE

ASSIGNMENT: Fill out the following questions, then read the passages listed on the day assigned, and answer the questions for each passage.

BY GOD'S GRACE, I WILL HAVE A DAILY DEVOTIONAL LIFE THIS WEEK. TIME ....

PLACE..

WHICH TRANSLATION ....

LENGTH OF TIME ....

Monday — Phil. 2:5 thru 10. Make note of the steps which took Jesus to his place of exaltation. How do these steps apply to us today?

Tuesday — Col. 1:14 thru 20. Substitute the name of Christ for the personal pronoun in the passage. What new insight did you receive from this reading?

Wednesday — John 15:1 thru 17. Who is the vine? Who are the branches? What does it mean to "abide?"

Thursday — Matt. 25:31 thru 46. How does this apply today?

Friday — Hebrews 12:1 thru 6. What do you feel is necessary for us to "finish the race?"

Saturday — Acts 2:14 thru 36. What were the most important facts which Peter covered in this sermon of his?

Sunday — Psalm 145. List the things the Psalmist was praising God for.

Suggestions For Further Study

Tapes 1517A "Quiet Time" and 1404 A B "Bible Study"

Quiet Time — Inter Varsity Press

Manna in the Morning by Stephen Olford, Moody Press

My Heart Christ's Home by Robert B. Munger, Billy Graham Evangelistic Association, Box 779, Minneapolis, Minn.

Time Alone With God, Billy Graham Evangelistic Association.

7 Minutes With God, The Navigators, Colorado Springs, Colorado.

Daily Devotional Diary (a reading plan with written reproduction) The Navigators.

CHAPTER V

THE LORDSHIP OF CHRIST
[Death to the Self-Life]

I. The Bible speaks of Jesus Christ as being Lord. He wants to be Lord of every believer's life.

The word Lord means: master, governer, chief, boss, ruler, sovereign. The term lordship indicates: ownership, absolute control, authority, rule, or dominion.

1. What right does Jesus Christ have to be Lord of our lives?

   Heb. 1:1, 2 ....

   Acts 2:36 ....

   John 13:13 ....

   I Cor. 6:20 ....

   John 15:5 ....

2. There are certain characteristics of a life in which Christ is the Lord. Match the proper characteristics with the supporting scripture:

Luke 9:23	( )	1. Not ashamed of the Gospel
Gal. 2:20	( )	2. Reflects Jesus
Rom. 1:16	( )	3. Obedient
Luke 6:46	( )	4. Self denied
Phil. 3:7, 8	( )	5. Love for others
John 8:31	( )	6. Transferred ownership
Gal. 5:22, 23	( )	7. Fruit of the Spirit evident
John 13:34, 35	( )	8. Continuing in the Word

3. There are certain practical steps we can take to make Christ the Lord of our lives. Some are listed below: Carefully study each step and then express in your own words what you think it means in a practical way in a person's life.

   A. John 12:24, 25 — death to the self life. ....

   ....

   ....

   ....

B. Romans 8:13 and Gal. 5:16, 17. We cannot commit suicide on a cross. The Holy Spirit can mortify (crucify) the flesh (self life). . . . .

. . . .

. . . .

C. We do have a choice. Romans 12:1, 2 . . . .

. . . .

. . . .

D. The choice is not once for all. Luke 9:23 . . . .

. . . .

. . . .

4. There are hindrances to Christ's Lordship. Read the verses and list each one next to the hindrance it refers to.

Mal. 3:8 _____ Priorities
Rom. 4:4-5 _____ Things (clothes, cars, etc.)
Luke 12:21 _____ Position
Luke 14:26 _____ Power
Prov. 16:32 _____ Pride
Heb. 12:15 _____ Family
II Tim. 1:7 _____ Escapism (alcohol, drugs)
Matt. 6:33 _____ Social life
Matt. 20:26 _____ Community service
Eccl. 5:10,11 _____ Pleasure
James 3:2 _____ Money
Prov. 23:7a _____ Sex
Prov. 14:30 _____ Worry
Matt. 7:1 _____ Self-effort
Rom. 12:3 _____ Robbing God
Luke 12:15 _____ Fear
Mark 4:19 _____ Thought life
Rom. 8:28 _____ Critical Spirit
I Peter 5:5-6 _____ Bitterness
Prov. 29:25; _____ Tongue
   Ps. 1:1
Prov. 23:29-35 _____ Envy
   (Living)
I Cor. 6:18-20; _____ Temper
   Matt. 5:27,28

5. From this list which two hindrances do you feel are the greatest today? ....
....

Circle the one you feel is your biggest problem at this time.

6. What will you do during this next week to allow God to deal with this area? How will you measure the results? (make it practical, personal and possible).

....
....
....
....
....

Suggestions For Further Study

Tape BSU 95 — "Lordship of Christ"
Tape 2165 — "Jesus Is Lord"
Tape 1206 — "The Lordship of Christ"
Tape 684 — "The Lordship of Christ"
True Discipleship, by William MacDonald, Walterick publishers

CHAPTER VI

THE IMPORTANCE OF GOD'S WORD
[THE HAND]
(Used by permission of The Navigators)

The "Word Hand" shows us the
five methods of learning from the
Bible. Each of these methods is important.

Hearing the Word from godly pastors and teachers provides us
insight into others' study of the Scriptures as well as stimulating
our own appetites for the Word.

Reading the Bible gives us an overall picture of God's Word.
Many find helpful a daily reading program which takes them
systematically through the Bible.

Studying the Scriptures leads us into personal discoveries of
God's truths. Writing down these discoveries helps us organize
and remember them better.

Memorizing God's Word enables us to use the sword of the Spirit
to overcome satan and temptations . . . to have it readily available for witnessing or helping others with a "word in season."

Meditation is the thumb of the Word Hand, for it is used in conjunction with each of the other four methods. Only as we meditate on God's Word — thinking of its meaning and application to our lives — will we discover its transforming power at work in us.

There are five basic ways we take in the Word of God. Since God is more interested in making us something than in simply teaching us something, (Eph. 1:12) how much of His Word we retain and apply is vitally important.

1. Match up the percentage of retention you feel would apply to each method of taking in the Word of God:

    | Hear | 1 | (|) 100% |
    | Read | 2 | (|) 25-60% |
    | Study | 3 | (|) 10-15% |
    | Memorize | 4 | (|) 15-25% |
    | Meditate | 5 | (|) 60-80% |

2. Write out the following verses in your own words and place the references on the proper portion of the hand illustration.

    A. Acts 17:11 . . . .
    . . . .
    . . . .
    . . . .
    . . . .

    B. Romans 10:17 . . . .
    . . . .
    . . . .

    C. Deut. 17:19 . . . .
    . . . .
    . . . .

    D. Psalm 1:2, 3 . . . .
    . . . .
    . . . .
    . . . .

    E. II Tim. 2:15 . . . .
    . . . .
    . . . .

F. Prov. 7:1-3 ....

....

....

G. Jer. 22:29 ....

....

....

H. I Tim. 4:15 ....

....

....

I. Rev. 1:3 ....

....

....

J. Psalm 119:9, 11 ....

....

....

....

3. How many of these five ways do you feel are vital for a growing Christian? ....

....

....

4. Just a word about each of the ways:
   A. Hearing — don't neglect the fellowship of believers. Hebrews 10:25.
   B. Reading — If you have never read through the Bible completely in a year, why not start now? Four chapters a day will more than put you through. From year to year, why not use different translations? They will help keep your reading fresh and allow God to reveal to you different facets of His truth.
   C. Studying — study differs from reading in several ways. To study, the following elements should be present:
      1. Original investigation.
      2. Written reproduction.
      3. Consistency.
      4. Personal Application (See page 37)
      5. "Pass-on-able" (it should be so real to our lives that we can pass it on to others.)
   We will be experiencing several types of Bible study farther on in this booklet.

D. Memorizing — scripture memory pays dividends. It is not easy. It reaches the sub-conscious levels of our very being. Pray before attempting it. You will need God's help. Memory courses are available from:

The Navigators, Box 1659, Colorado Springs, Colorado

Moody Press, 820 N. LaSalle St., Chicago, Illinois

Bible Memory Association
P.O. Box 12,000
St. Louis, Missouri 63112

E. Meditation — this is spiritual digestion. It is getting the Word of God from the head to the heart and into the life.
Why not pray over the verses you are memorizing phrase by phrase as a form of meditation, or why not personalize the scripture as it is below for your meditation time:

Col. 3:10-16

"I am living a brand new kind of life that is continually learning more and more what is right, and trying constantly to be more and more like Christ who created this new life within me. In this new life, one's nationality or race or education or social position is not important; such things mean nothing — whether a person has Christ is what matters, and He is equally available to all. Since I have been chosen by God, who has given me this new kind of life, and because of His deep love and concern for me, I should practice tender hearted mercy and kindness to others. I should not worry about making a good impression on them, but be ready to suffer quietly and patiently. I should be gentle and ready to forgive, never holding grudges, and remembering that the Lord forgave me, so I must forgive others. I should let love guide my life, for then the whole church will stay together in perfect harmony. I will let the peace of heart which comes from Christ be always present in my heart and life, for this is my responsibility and privilege as a member of His Body, and I should always be thankful. I want to remember what Christ has taught and let His words enrich my life and make me wise. I would like to teach them to others and to sing them out in psalms and hymns and spiritual songs, singing to the Lord from a thankful heart."

5. Which way of scripture intake do you feel is most needed in your life currently? . . . .

6. What will you do in the next seven days to start correcting this lack? (every journey is made by taking the first step — make a start) . . . .
. . . .
. . . .
. . . .
. . . .

Suggestions For Further Study

Tape 1595 — "Intake of the Word"
Tape 1955 — "Scripture Memory"
Tape 820 — "Scripture Memory"
Tape 258 — "Bible Study"
Primer on Meditation, by The Navigators, Colorado Springs, Colorado

HOW TO MAKE A PERSONAL
APPLICATION FROM BIBLE STUDY

A. **What impresses me most?**
   (Generally, as you study a subject or a portion, God by His Spirit will lay some particular aspect on your heart. Pray that God will open your eyes to a specific application. Ask Him what He wants you to do about it.)

B. **Where do I fall short in this?**
   (When God speaks to you about a particular aspect of this study, write out the place where you fall short in this area. Use personal singular pronouns, I, Me, etc. An application should be *personal, practical and possible.* It should be concerned with a truth which may be translated into daily life and should be clearly stated. The application may deal with your relation to God or your relation to man. It should result in personal spiritual enrichment and uplifting by deepening your relationship to the Lord, or should improve your relationship to fellow Christians or those outside Christ.)

C. **What do I intend to do about it, with God's help?**
   (Write out your intention as a definite action that you will take now to correct the weakness, build the needed quality into your life, strengthen the understanding, etc. This action may be memorizing a verse on the subject, or making a special study on it, or praying daily about the need. It may be writing a letter of apology, righting some harm done, etc. Whatever the action — *be specific.*)

THE GODLY MAN
AS
CHRIST'S
REPRESENTATIVE

Study this picture and be prepared to answer the following questions about it.

1. What does the picture say to you? . . . .
   . . . .
   . . . .

2. Why is he there? . . . .
   . . . .

3. What is he thinking? . . . .
   . . . .
   . . . .

4. Who cares about him? . . . .

Study this picture and be prepared to answer the following questions about it.

1. What is going on in the picture? . . . .
   . . . .
   . . . .
   . . . .

2. Where is it happening? . . . .
   . . . .
   . . . .

3. What is the crowd's reaction? . . . .
   . . . .
   . . . .

4. Who do you most identify with in the picture? . . . .
   . . . .
   . . . .

CHAPTER VII

BIBLICAL EXAMPLE — ABRAHAM

This lesson (on Abraham) is a type of character study. This is a very interesting and rewarding way of studying Biblical personalities. To encourage and aid you in doing other such studies on your own from the Bible, a sample outline you might wish to follow is included here:

Character Study Outline:

1. List all the characteristics (good and bad) of the person to be studied.
2. Check a concordance to get verses of Scripture on these characteristics. (For instance: if the person was obedient to God, find a verse that speaks of the blessings of obedience; if the person lied or hurt others by the use of his tongue, find a verse that tells what God thinks of wrong use of the tongue; if the person believed God for great things, find a verse that tells the value God places on such belief, etc.)
3. Write a thumb-nail sketch or a brief summary of the person's life.
4. Write out problems. These can be things you don't understand about the person, or things you don't understand about God's dealings with him. State in the form of questions.
5. State what you think is the leading lesson taught by this life.
6. Make a personal application. (See page 37 for explanation.)

ABRAHAM — Genesis 11:25

Reference Scriptures:

Gen. 11:29-31
Gen. 12:1, 2, 4, 8, 10, 12-16-19, 20
Gen. 13:1, 2, 4-9, 15, 18
Gen. 14:14-16, 20, 22
Gen. 15:1, 2, 6, 8, 12-15
Gen. 16:1-4
Gen. 17:1, 3, 5, 11, 12, 15, 17, 23
Gen. 18:4-6, 13, 15, 19, 23-32
Gen. 19:27
Gen. 20:2-6, 11, 12

Gen. 21:2-4, 8, 11, 12, 14, 22-31
Gen. 22:1-3, 8, 16
Gen. 23:2, 6, 7, 13
Gen. 24:3, 4
Gen. 25:5

I. List all the characteristics and attitudes you see in his life—both good and bad.

....
....
....
....
....
....
....
....
....

II. List at least five of the above characteristics. From your own knowledge of the Bible, or using a concordance, find a cross-reference for each one. (See explanation on page 42, Number 2)

Characteristic   Cross-Reference

....
....
....
....
....
....
....

III. Write a brief summary of his life:

....
....
....
....
....
....
....
....
....
....
....
....

IV. What problems do you find in understanding either God's dealing with Abraham or his response to God or other people?

....
....
....

. . . .
. . . .

V. What do you think were some of this man's attitudes

A. Toward God? . . . .
. . . .
. . . .

B. Toward his wife? . . . .
. . . .
. . . .

C. Toward his children? . . . .
. . . .
. . . .

VI. What would you say is the leading lesson taught by his life?
. . . .
. . . .
. . . .
. . . .

VII. What key insight about God did you discover while studying the life of Abraham?
. . . .
. . . .
. . . .
. . . .
. . . .

VIII. What trait do you see in Abraham that you would like to see in your own life?
. . . .

XI. Using the outline on page 37, write out what action you will take this week to make a personal application from this study.

A. What impresses me most? . . . .
. . . .

B. Where do I fall short in this? . . . .
. . . .
. . . .

C. What do I intend to do about it, with God's help?
. . . .
. . . .
. . . .
. . . .

Study this picture and be prepared to answer the following questions about it.

1. What does the picture symbolize to you? . . . .
. . . .
. . . .

2. How could it relate to Christian character? . . . .
. . . .
. . . .
. . . .

3. If you could change the picture, how would you do it? . . . .
. . . .
. . . .
. . . .
. . . .
. . . .

Study this picture and be prepared to answer the following questions about it:

1. What does the picture mean to you? ....

   ....

2. How does it relate to a guidance system in life? ....

   ....

3. Why do you think the picture was taken? ....

   ....

   ....

   ....

   ....

CHAPTER VIII

CHARACTER & GUIDANCE SYSTEM OF A DISCIPLE
[THE BICYCLE]

In Psalm 78:71, 72, we read of God's calling David to be His people's shepherd (king). The testimony is that David cared for them in integrity of heart and with skillful hands. In the illustration of the Bicycle, "skillful hands" represents the back wheel. "Integrity of heart" represents the front wheel which is the character and guidance system of a disciple. It is possible to live the first year of the Christian life 20 times, instead of living 20 years of the Christian life. To insure that this does not happen, a person needs not only skill, but goals and guidance.

1. What should be the overall objective of the Christian regarding the world? Matt. 28:19, 20 . . . .
. . . .
. . . .

2. What is God's objective and will for every believer? Romans 8:29 . . . .
. . . .

II Peter 3:18 . . . .
. . . .

3. Write the key thought you see in each of the following
   Scriptures.

   Phil. 4:8 ....

   Joshua 14:10, 12 ....

   Heb. 10:36 ....

   I Cor. 16:13 ....

   Eph. 4:13 ....

   Col. 1:18 ....

   II Cor. 10:5 ....

   Ps. 18:29 ....

   Rev. 2:10 ....

   II Cor. 4:16 ....

   Gal. 4:19 ....

   II Cor. 3:18 ....

   Phil. 1:21 ....

   Place the above Scripture references under the proper
   heading below.

   POSITIVE MENTAL   DRIVE
         ATTITUDE   ....
   ....
   ....
   ....
   ....

      PERSISTENCE   MATURE
   ....   PERSONALITY
   ....
   ....
   ....
   ....

4. Many factors combine to determine the character and guidance system of a disciple. Read the Scripture then place each of the traits of character in one of the four categories listed below:

Reliance on Christ II Cor. 3:5
Faith in Christ Phil. 4:13
Trust in Christ Job 23:10
Dependance on
    Christ Rom. 8:28
Expectancy Phil 4:19
Cheerfulness Prov. 15:15
Enthusiasm Judges 6:25-27
Initiative I Kings 18:21
Decisiveness James 1:8
    I Cor. 14:8
Faithfulness Luke 16:10
    Prov. 25:19

Patience Heb. 6:15
Steadfastness Eph. 6:13
Courage Dan. 3:16-18
Self Control I Cor. 9:26, 27
Servant Heart I Cor. 9:19
Submissiveness to
    Authority I Peter 5:5, 6
Teachableness Prov. 10:8
Peacemaker Psalm 133:1
Acceptance of
    Others I Cor. 4:5
Humility Phil. 2:3-4

POSITIVE MENTAL ATTITUDE

. . . .
. . . .
. . . .
. . . .
. . . .
. . . .
. . . .
. . . .

DRIVE

. . . .
. . . .
. . . .
. . . .
. . . .
. . . .
. . . .

PERSISTENCE

. . . .
. . . .
. . . .
. . . .
. . . .
. . . .
. . . .
. . . .

MATURE PERSONALITY

. . . .
. . . .
. . . .
. . . .
. . . .
. . . .
. . . .

5. While it is true that God has made each of us different and unique in personality, it is equally true that there are certain qualities we all need. Which two of the traits of character would you most like to see strengthened in your own life? . . . .

. . . .

Why these two? . . . .

. . . .

. . . .

. . . .

. . . .

The Christian life is like riding a bicycle in many respects. If you don't move on, you will fall off. There are three main areas which cause people to falter in their Christian walk. They are the psychological, physical and the spiritual. A number of problems are caused because Christians lack a basic understanding of the emotional facts of what it means to walk with God. It does not mean that we will always have perfect peace. II Cor. 6:10. Further, psychological conflict is not abnormal or sinful, but failure to resolve the conflict may be.

6. Match the scripture references with the psychological problems which can cause people to "fall off" in the Christian life.

YOU'RE BOUND TO HEAR A DISCOURAGING WORD SOMETIMES.

( )   Wrong mind set
( )   Fear
( )   Production oriented
( )   Worldiness
( )   Guilt
( )   Disappointment with God
( )   Disappointment with others
( )   Disappointment with self
( )   Playing to wrong audience
( )   Bitterness and rebellion

1. Luke 10:20
2. I Jn. 2:15, 16
3. II Tim. 1:7
4. Heb. 12:2
5. Romans 13:1, 2
6. John 5:44
7. Heb. 12:15
8. Jer. 17:5-9
9. Phil. 3:3
10. Psalm 38:4
11. Psalm 37:34

7. Select two from the above list and explain in your own words how you would deal with them in your life or the life of another: ....

....

....

....

....

....

....

....

....

....

....

PHYSICAL:

8. An ineffective Christian walk may sometimes be traced to a physical root. List some of these causes below and their solutions:

CAUSE	SOLUTIONS
Heb. 6:12	II Tim. 2:3, 4 ....
	....
Dan. 7:25a	Ps. 71:18 ....
	....
I Cor. 15:33	Prov. 13:20 ....
	....
Prov. 21:5	Mark 6:31 & Is. 28:16 ......
	....
	....

SPIRITUAL:

9. The psychological, physical, and spiritual lives are interdependent in most people. A few spiritual warnings are to be found in the following verses:

Name them:

I Cor. 10:12 ....

John 15:5 ....

I Peter 2:1, 2 ....

I Cor. 4:7 ....

I Peter 5:8 ....

I Peter 5:5, 6 ....

10. The following remedies may be helpful in encouraging you to maintain balance and momentum in your Christian life:

    A. Make a genuine and total cómmitment of your life to God.

    B. Apply the necessary disciplines to walk with God in His Word, prayer and keeping short accounts with Him (keeping known sins confessed).

    C. Faith in the following:

        1. The sovereignty of God (He is in control) Ps. 115:3.

        2. The power of God (He can do anything) Jer. 32:17.

        3. The knowledge of God (He knows what is going on) Heb. 4:13.

        4. He is personally interested in you. John 10:3, 4; Luke 12:7.

    D. Maintain the vessel. I Cor. 9:26, 27. (A person in good physical and psychological condition will be in better shape spiritually).

    E. Be submissive to God rather than rebellious. James 4: 6, 7.

    F. Try daily to be obedient to Him. I Sam. 15:22, 23; I Peter 3:10, 11.

    G. Try to put to use any truth you learn (walk in the light) I John 1:7.

    H. Try to profit from discipline or testing. Heb. 5:8, Heb. 12:6, Rev. 3:19.

    I. Have a goal of becoming spiritually educated through Bible study. Col. 1:9, 10, Col. 2:2, 3.

    J. Permit yourself to be exhorted or rebuked by other Christians when needed. Gal. 6:1, I Tim. 5:20, Heb. 10:25.

    K. Acquire the habit of intelligent and bold prayer. Eph. 6:18.

    L. Fight the good fight of faith. Prov. 3:5, I Peter 4:19, I Peter 5:7.

11. Review the 12 suggestions above and list the two you feel

most needed in your life at this time. . . . .

. . . .

. . . .

. . . .

. . . .

. . . .

. . . .

12. How, spiritually, do you fail in these two areas? . . . .

. . . .

. . . .

. . . .

. . . .

A. What will you do about them this coming week? . . . .

. . . .

. . . .

. . . .

. . . .

B. How will you check up on yourself? . . . .

. . . .

Suggestions for Further Study
Tape — BSU 155A — "Characteristics of a Disciple"
Spirit-Controlled Temperament and **Transformed Tempera-ments,** by Dr. Tim LaHaye, Tyndale House

Study this picture and be prepared to answer the following
questions about it.

1. What does the picture say to you? . . . .

    . . . .

·2. How do you relate to the picture? . . . .

    . . . .

3. What lesson would you draw from it to share with others? . .

    . . . .

    . . . .

    . . . .

Study this picture and be prepared to answer the following questions about it.

1.   What does this picture remind you of? ....
....
....

2.   How can you see yourself in the picture? ....
....
....
....

3.   What does the picture say to you? ....
....
....

Study this picture and be prepared to answer the following
questions about it.

1.   How do you react to the picture? . . . .
. . . .
. . . .

2.   How do you feel about it? . . . .
. . . .

3.   What do the two chairs mean? . . . .
. . . .
. . . .

Study this picture and be prepared to answer the following questions about it.

1. What is happening in the picture? . . . .
    . . . .

2. What is the baby thinking? . . . .
    . . . .

3. If he could talk, what would he say? . . . .
    . . . .

4. How does this picture relate to the preceding picture? . .
    . . . .
    . . . .

CHAPTER IX

PRIORITIES, GOALS AND THE USE OF TIME

Today it seems that very few people feel they have enough time. There are some basic facts we need to know:

1. We all have the same amount of time.
2. We have all the time we need.
3. When we are pressured by time, it means either:
   A. We are doing the wrong things.
   B. We are doing the right things in the wrong way.

I. What do you learn about time and its use from Psalm 90:9 thru 12? . . . .
. . . .
. . . .
. . . .
. . . .
. . . .

II. Define time: . . . .
. . . .
. . . .
. . . .

III. Hebrews 1:2 (Amplified), "(But) in the last of these days He has spoken to us in (the person of a) Son, Whom He appointed Heir and lawful Owner of all things, also by and **through Whom He created** the worlds and the reaches of space and the **ages of time** — (that is), He made, produced, built, operated and arranged them in order."
Where did time come from? . . . .

IV. Whose time is it anyway? I Cor. 6:19, 20
CHECK ONE: Christ's ( ) Ours ( ) Everybody's ( )

V. According to I Cor. 4:2, we are . . . . of our time also. Explain what stewardship of time means. . . . . . .
. . . .
. . . .
. . . .

VI. What do the following verses teach us regarding time from our point of view?

Psalm 39:4,   James 4:14   Psalm 90:9

. . . .

. . . .

. . . .

. . . .

. . . .

. . . .

. . . .

. . . .

VII. Psalm 90:10 says our normal life span should be 70 years. How many days do you now have left? . . . .
What percentage of your life is already passed? . . . .

. . . .

In your imagination, project your life to its end. Now look back and decide what you would have wanted your life to have meant? This will assist you in setting priorities and goals.

VIII. Below are listed some areas of priorities with two scriptures for each of them. First match the scriptures with the areas. Then number the areas in the order of their importance as you think God sees them.

PRIORITY	AREAS			VERSES
( )	Wife	( ) ( )		1. Prov. 22:6
( )	Home	( ) ( )		2. Matt. 22:37, 38
( )	Personal walk with Christ	( ) ( )		3. I Tim. 5:8
				4. I Cor. 1:9
( )	Ministry & Outreach	( ) ( )		5. Col. 3:23
				6. II Thess. 3:11, 12
( )	Recreation	( ) ( )		7. Gen. 2:24
( )	Children	( ) ( )		8. II Cor. 5:19, 20
( )	Public relations (what others think)	( ) ( )		9. Mark 6:31
				10. I Tim. 6:17
				11. Matt. 28:18-20
				12. Prov. 29:25
				13. Gal. 1:10

IX. If you feel your life style is not agreeing with priorities as God views them, what will you do specifically in one area this week to help re-align your life style to fit God's priorities? . . . .

. . . .
. . . .
. . . .
. . . .

STRONG PEOPLE HAVE GOALS, WEAK PEOPLE ONLY HAVE WISHES.

X. Search the following verses and select a basic pre-requisite for goal setting from each one. Write out the principle as you discover it from each verse.

Prov. 16:9 (Living) "We should make plans — counting on God to direct us." PRINCIPLE DISCOVERED . . . .

. . . .
. . . .
. . . .
. . . .

Prov. 23:23 (Living) "Get the facts at any price, and hold on tightly to all the good sense you can get." PRINCIPLE DISCOVERED: . . . .

. . . .

Acts 6:10 (Williams) "But they could not cope with his good practical sense and the spiritual power with which he usually spoke." PRINCIPLE DISCOVERED: . . . .

. . . .
. . . .

XI. Place the following verses (written out below) under their proper headings in goal preparation.

Verses:

I Kings 3:23 (Living) "Then the king said, 'let's get the facts straight: both of you claim the living child, and each says that the dead child belongs to the other."

Prov. 22:3 (Living), "A prudent man foresees the difficulties ahead and **prepares** for them; the simpleton goes blindly on and **suffers** consequences."

Prov. 11:14 (New English Bible) "For want of skillful strategy an army is lost. Victory is the fruit of long planning."

I Kings 18:21 (Living), "Then Elijah talked to them. 'How long are you going to waver between two opinions?' he asked the people. If the Lord is God, follow him! But if Baal is God, then follow him!"

HEADINGS	VERSES
Plan ahead	
Get the facts	
Use your head	
Make a decision	

1. Plan your time — if you don't, others will.
2. Leave a margin — for the unexpected.
3. Do one thing at a time and finish it.
4. Learn to say "NO." Giving an unqualified no answer is a mark of Christian maturity.
5. Separate the important from the urgent.
6. Use short cuts and helps which promote efficiency.
7. Be decisive. Do not be paralyzed by indecision.
8. Write it down. The poorest pencil has a better memory than the sharpest mind.
9. Be time conscious.

ASSIGNMENT:
Write out some of your current goals in the following areas and be prepared to share them:

1. Personal (spiritual, mental, emotional, physical, and social) ....

....

....

....

....

....

2. Family (wife, children and parents) ....

....

....

....

....

....

3. Vocation (job advancement, new work, economic goals, etc.) ....
....
....
....
....
....

4. Ministry (church, outreach, Bible study) ....
....
....
....
....
....
....

5. Recreational (sports, vacations, etc.) ....
....
....
....
....
....
....

6. Public Relations (community involvement, school participation, etc.) ....
....
....
....
....
....
....

Suggestions For Further Study
Tape 1273 AB — "Priorites and the Use of Time"
Tyranny of the Urgent — Intervarsity Press

Study this picture and be prepared to answer the following questions about it.

1. What is the man doing? . . . .
    . . . .
2. Why is he doing it? . . . .
    . . . .
3. What does the picture say to you? . . . .
    . . . .
4. How can you see yourself in it? . . . .
    . . . .
    . . . .
    . . . .

Study this picture and be prepared to answer the following
questions about it.

1. How is the globe symoblic? . . . .
    . . . .

2. What do you think the picture means? . . . .
    . . . .
    . . . .
    . . . .

3. What does it say to you? . . . .
    . . . .
    . . . .
    . . . .
    . . . .

CHAPTER X

FINDING GOD'S WILL

God is more interested in our knowing and doing His will than we are in discovering it. He is not trying to hide His will from us. His will is never in opposition to His Word.

I. God's revealed will is:
   1. I Tim. 2:4 . . . .
      . . . .
   2. I Thess. 4:3 . . . .
      . . . .
   3. Gal. 1:4 . . . .
      . . . .
   4. I Thess. 5:18 . . . .
      . . . .
   5. I Peter 2:15 . . . .
   6. I Peter 4:19 . . . .
   7. Romans 14:9 . . . .

II. Principles in determining right or wrong.
   Christianity is not a set of rules but the operation of Divine principles. Some things are clear as to their rightness or wrongness as revealed in the Bible. Other areas are not as clear. These areas need careful examination and decision by each of us.

Mark the following statements true or false in light of the Scriptures given.

1. If the Bible doesn't specifically condemn it, it is all right for me to do. I Cor. 6:12   T . . . F . . .

2. If the Bible speaks against it, I must not do it. Acts 5:29   T . . . F . . .

3. If it is socially acceptable, it is all right. Gal. 1:10   T . . . F . . .

4. If it could hurt my body, I must not do it. I Cor. 6:19, 20   T . . . F . . .

5. How it affects others is not really important. Romans 14:21, II Cor. 6:3, I Cor. 11:1, I Cor. 10:33   T... F...

6. I should be concerned with whether it glorifies God or not. I Cor. 10:31   T... F...

7. I am responsible for how it affects my mind. Phil. 2:5   T... F...

8. If it is my time, life or money, I am investing, then it is my own business. I Cor. 4:2   T... F...

III. Discovering God's will.

1. In Gensis 24:27, Abraham's servant was led by God because he was: (underline the correct answer)

   A. A godly man
   B. Wise
   C. Moving in the direction of discovering God's will
   D. Jewish

2. Psalm 119:105 teaches that clear leading for a life comes from ....
....

3. Another way God leads us is through Prov. 11:14 ....

4. Prov. 16:33 (Amplified) "The lot is cast into the lap, but the decision is wholly of the Lord — even the events (that seem accidental) are really ordered by Him," indicates that God can lead us through:
                    (underline one)
   A. Throwing dice
   B. Accidents
   C. Circumstances

5. The inner conviction that a certain course of action is right is called in Phil. 4:6, 7 ....

We have discovered that God leads us through His Word, circumstances, inner peace and Godly counsel. He also leads those who are moving instead of sitting still. Remember, the most reliable leading is always the Bible.

IV. <u>Procedures for discovering God's will.</u> Study the following outline carefully and keep it handy as a reference for discovering God's will for your own life or helping another to determine what God would have him to do.

PROCEDURE FOR DISCOVERING GOD'S WILL

1. Do you believe that God's will can be known definitely and accurately? If not, look up Ps. 32:8 and Is. 30:21.
2. Are you willing to seek God's will and do it or would you just like to have an option on it? John 7:17
3. Have you made a permanent decision of commitment to be yielded to God for the rest of your life? If not, meditate on Rom. 12:1, 2 and seek counsel.
4. Is there any known unconfessed sin in your life? If so, stop here and confess it and forsake it. If you won't do that, then do not proceed in seeking God's will. I John 1:9, Prov. 28:13, Ps. 66:18
5. Are you obeying the known will of God for your life on a daily basis? If not, start today and demonstrate it before proceeding. Ps. 119:59, 60
6. Are you in neutral, willing for the matter to fall either way? Ask God to reveal whether you are in neutral. If not, continue to pray that God's desires will be your desires. Phil. 2:13
7. Are you praying specifically and definitely about it in faith? Make a list of your specific thoughts and pray about them. Pray in faith. James 1:5-7 (Living) Mark 10:51
8. Are you fellowshipping with God daily through reading His Word and prayer? If not, commit yourself to begin today. Ps. 5:3
9. Has God spoken to you through His Word, in your regular reading, or your scripture review? Keep a written record of what God speaks to you about. If you have been in the Word and have no guidance from it, continue in the Word but wait. Ps. 37:34 (Living)
10. Do you have *all* the available facts? If not, take action to get the facts. Prov. 24:3, 4 (Living)

11. Make a list here of advantages and disadvantages about the issue:

ADVANTAGES

. . . .
. . . .
. . . .
. . . .
. . . .
. . . .

DISADVANTAGES

. . . .
. . . .
. . . .
. . . .
. . . .
. . . .

12. What does common sense tell you to do? Acts 6:10 (Williams)
13. What do you want to do? Ps. 37:4
14. Why do you want to do it? Prov. 21:2 (Living)
15. Is it of benefit to you (spiritually, physically, emotionally, mentally, socially)? I Cor. 6:12
16. Will it be a thorn causing anxious cares, desire for riches, or desire for pleasure? Mark 4:19, Luke 8:14
17. Will it be a weight? Heb. 12:1, 2
18. Will it cause another to stumble? I Cor. 10:23, Rom. 14:21. Will it glorify God? I Cor. 10:31
19. Have you asked counsel from three spiritually mature people? If so, record what they said. If not, write the names of three you can ask:
   1. . . . .
   2. . . . .
   3. . . . .
   Prov. 15:22
20. Does it violate any known scriptural principle? Ps. 119:19 (Living)
21. Are you willing to wait in faith for God to line up His Word, your peace, and circumstances? Heb. 10:36
22. Do you have inner conviction or peace about a course of action? If so, proceed with conviction. Rom. 14:23

23. Act in faith, believing God wants you to do it. Heb. 11:6

V. Application: Review the principles in determing right or
wrong. In the light of these principles, what are you now
doing which you should stop or what are you considering
doing which you should reject? What will you do about it?

. . . .
. . . .
. . . .
. . . .
. . . .
. . . .

Suggestions For Further Study

Tape 258A — "Will of God"

Tape 1533 — "Will of God"

Affirming the Will of God by Paul E. Little — Intervarsity
Press

How to Know God's Will by Marion H. Nelson — Moody Press

Study this picture and be prepared to answer the following questions about it:

1. What is the picture saying? ....
   ....
   ....
2. How did he get in such a shape? ....
   ....
   ....
3. What advice would you give him? ....
   ....
   ....
   ....
   ....

Study this picture and be prepared to answer the following questions about it:

1. What does it symbolize to you? . . . .
. . . .

2. How did he get in that shape? . . . .
. . . .

3. How can he escape? . . . .
. . . .

4. Do you ever feel like you are bound? . . . .
   Explain . . . .
. . . .
. . . .
. . . .
. . . .

Study this picture and be prepared to answer the following questions about it:

1. Why is he happy? . . . .
. . . .

2. What thoughts does a family budget bring to your mind? . . . . .
. . . .
. . . .

3. What has he been doing? . . . .
. . . .
. . . .
. . . .
. . . .

Sudy this picture and be prepared to answer the following questions about it:

1. Who do you think owns the cards? . . . .
. . . .
. . . .

2. Why do you think he carries them? . . . .
. . . .
. . . .
. . . .

3. What problems, if any, do you sense in this picture? . . . .
. . . .
. . . .
. . . .

4. How does the picture relate to you? . . . .
. . . .
. . . .
. . . .

CHAPTER XI

FINANCIAL RESPONSIBILITY

Money represents life because we must invest our lives to acquire it. Money is neither good nor bad, but becomes so only in the context of its use. It is a medium of exchange. Since it represents life, we are responsible for its use and handling. I Cor. 4:2, "Moreover it is required in stewards, that a man be found faithful."

I. Financial truths.
    1. Who really owns the world's riches? Haggai 2:8 . . . .

    . . . .

    2. Who gives us our ability to make money? Deut. 8:18, I Cor. 4:7 . . . .

    3. Match up some of the pitfalls of money with their appropriate scriptures:

(   ) Forgetting God . . . .   1. Prov. 30:8, 9
(   ) Stop trusting God . . . .   2. I Tim. 6:10
(   ) Being deceived . . . .   3. Mark 4:19
(   ) Falling in love with money . . . . . .   4. Deut. 8:12-14
(   ) Trusting a fleeting commodity . . .   5. Prov. 23:4, 5
(   ) Becoming ungrateful . . . .   6. Matt. 6:24
(   ) Becoming double minded . . . .   7. Mal. 3:8
(   ) Robbing God . . . .   8. Prov. 11:28 (Living)

        "Trust in your money and down you go!
        Trust in God and flourish as a tree."

    4. Do you feel prosperity or poverty is more spiritually helpful? . . . .
       Why? . . . .

    . . . .

    5. List a principle in finances from the following scriptures: Prov. 20:4, Prov. 14:23, II Thess. 3:10
       The principle is: . . . .

    . . . .

6. Prov. 21:20 (Living) says, "The wise man saves for the future, but the foolish man spends whatever he gets." What principle do we find in this verse regarding finances? . . . .

. . . .

7. Prov. 16:9 (Living) says, "We should make plans — counting on God to direct us." How does this apply in finances? . . . .

. . . .

8. Prov. 17:18 (Living) says, "It is poor judgment to countersign another's note, to become responsible for his debts." What does this warn us against? . . . .

. . . .

9. What is our condition when we owe money? Prov. 22:7 .

. . . .

. . . .

10. Many people stay in debt because of a continuing practice of buying items which depreciate rapidly. Watch out for this trap. Romans 13:8 says we are to owe others only . . . .

. . . .

. . . .

11. God, in Phil. 4:19, has promised to provide our . . . .

. . . .

12. What is the difference between wants and needs? . . . . . .

. . . .

13. In Matthew 4:6, 7, the devil tempted Jesus to the sin of presumption. How can this sin be committed in the financial realm? . . . .

. . . .

. . . .

. . . .

. . . .

14. If you are short of money, answering the following questions may reveal to you the reason why this is true:
   A. Do I really need it?
   B. Is God testing my faith?
   C. Did I mis-spend the money God has already given me?
   D. Have I violated the financial principles?
   Match the scriptures with the principles:
   ( )   Stinginess   1. Luke 12:15
   ( )   Hastiness   2. Prov. 11:24, 25
   ( )   Stubbornness   3. Prov. 28:19, 20
   ( )   Laziness   4. Prov. 21:5
   ( )   Gluttony   5. Prov. 20:13
   ( )   Craftiness   6. Prov. 23:21
   ( )   Coveteousness   7. Prov. 13:18

II. Another important principle in finances is giving. We will search for truths regarding why, how, and where to give.
   1. In the light of Deut. 14:23b (Living), "the purpose of tithing is to teach you always to put God first in your lives." Why do you feel God instituted tithing? . . . .
   . . . .
   . . . .

God is not nearly as interested in raising money as He is in raising children.

   2. What has God promised to those who give faithfully? Malachi 3:10 . . . .
   3. What would be the opposite effect which could come upon those who do not give faithfully? Malachi 3:11 . . .
   . . . .
   . . . .
   4. List some principles of giving to be found in II Cor. 9:6 thru 15. . . . .
   . . . .
   . . . .
   5. List some principles of giving to be found in II Cor. 8:1 thru 15 . . . .
   . . . .
   . . . .
   . . . .

6. Where should we give?
   A. Gal. 6:6 . . . .
   B. Prov. 19:17 . . . .
   C. James 2:15, 16 . . . .
   D. I Cor. 9:11-14 . . . .
   . . . .

ASSIGNMENT:

In the light of this study, discuss your financial situation with your wife to see if some changes need to be made. If they do, and you are in agreement, put them into effect immediately.

Suggestions For Further Study

Tape 1267 AB — "Financial Responsibility"

How to Live on your Income, Readers Digest Association, Pleasantville, New York

Guide to Personal Finance by Sal Nuccio, Harper & Row Publishers

Study this picture and be prepared to answer the following questions about it:

1. Who are the people? . . . .

. . . .

2. Why are they on print? . . . .

. . . .

3. Why are they faceless? . . . .

. . . .

4. What does the picture really mean? . . . .

. . . .

. . . .

. . . .

. . . .

CHAPTER XII

THE CHURCH

1. Define the church in your own words . . . .
. . . .
. . . .
. . . .

2. Who owns the church? Acts 20:28 . . . .
. . . .

3. Who is the head of the church? Col. 1:18 . . . .

4. What is God's desire for the church? I Cor. 1:9, 10 and Eph.
5:26, 27 . . . .

5. What has God promised to give His people? Jeremiah 3:15 . . .
. . . .

6. What are these spiritual leaders to do? Acts 20:28 . . . .
. . . .
. . . .
. . . .

   I Peter 5:2 . . . .
. . . .

7. What is to be a spiritual leader's attitude? . . . .
Luke 22:26 . . . .
Mark 10:45 . . . .

8. What was the man's problem in Psa. 142:4? . . . .
. . . .
. . . .

9. Who is caring for your soul? . . . .
According to I Cor. 4:15, we have many teachers, but only one
spiritual parent. Write the name of the one person you
look to for spiritual leadership more than any other . . . .
. . . .

10. What should your response to your spiritual leader be? . . . . . .
    Hebrews 13:17 . . . .
    I Thess. 5:12, 13 . . . .
11. What do we learn from I Cor. 12:4-18 about what part we are
    to play in the operation of the church? . . . .
    . . . .
    . . . .
12. What does Hebrews 10:25 mean to you in the context of your
    church? . . . .
    . . . .
13. If we are not in agreement with spiritual leadership, what
    must we watch out for? I Sam. 24:6, I Chron. 16:22 . . . .
    . . . .
    . . . .
    . . . .
14. Whose responsibility is it to choose who fills the positions
    of spiritual leadership? Psa. 75:6, 7 . . . .
    . . . .

I Tim. 1:5 in the 20th Century New Testament says, "The object of all instruction is to
call forth that love which comes from a pure
heart, a clear conscience, and a sincere faith"
and indicates that any instruction we are
giving or receiving in the Christian context
should eventuate in love.

15. What must a servant of God guard against? II Tim. 2:24, 25
    . . . .
    . . . .
    . . . .
    . . . .

ASSIGNMENT:
Gal. 5:22, 23 lists the fruit of the spirit. Meditate over these verses
and ask God to show you how you have fallen short of them in
your church relationship. Will you allow Him to correct this by
expressing Himself through you in the situation this coming
week? How? . . . .
. . . .
. . . .
. . . .

....
....
....
....
....
....
....
....
....

Suggestions For Further Study

Tape 602 — "The Servant Church"
Tape 603 — "The Teaching Church"

Study this picture and be prepared to answer the following questions about it.

1. What does the picture say to you? . . . .

   . . . .
2. Where is he? . . . .
3. What is he doing? . . . .
4. What is he thinking? . . . .
5. What is he feeling? . . . .
6. What could you do to help him? . . . .

   . . . .

   . . . .

   . . . .

Study this picture and be prepared to answer the following questions about it.

1. What has happened? . . . .
. . . .

2. What is the problem? . . . .
. . . .

3. What could you do to help? . . . .
. . . .
. . . .

4. How do you feel about it? . . . .
. . . .
. . . .

Study this picture and be prepared to answer the following questions about it.

1. What is happening? ....

....

2. What is causing her problem? ....

....

3. What is she feeling? ....

....

4. How could you help? ....

....

....

Study this picture and be prepared to answer the following questions about it.

1. What is going on? ....
   ....

2. Why is the little boy doing it? ....
   ....
   ....

3. What lesson do you see in the picture? ....
   ....
   ....

CHAPTER XIII

HELPING OTHERS

Follow-up is parental care for spiritual babes. It is spiritual pediatrics. It means accepting spiritual responsibility for those God brings to you for help.

1. The book of I Thessalonians is a great revelation and exposition of follow-up principles. Read the book carefully, inserting the proper scripture references opposite the stated follow-up principle:

   The objective of follow-up . . . .

   Personal example . . . .

   Individual care . . . .

   Heart involvement . . . .

   Practical helps . . . .

   Prayer . . . .

   Sharing of the life . . . .

   Godly teaching . . . .

2. Various means of follow-up are available to us today, which were available to the early church. List some of them from the following verses:

   I Cor. 4:17 . . . .

   I Jn. 2:1, 2 . . . .

   Phil. 1:3, 4 . . . .

   Acts 15:36 . . . .

3. Since God is not as interested in how many we are as how much we count, spiritual maturity is a crying need. The Bible gives us examples of deeper relationships than merely follow-up. In these relationships, the imparting of life and encouraging to maximum maturity was taking place. Name the people involved in this type of deeper training, from the following passages:

   II Tim. 2:2 . . . .

   Acts 20:4 . . . .

   II Kings 2:6 . . . .

   Exodus 24:13 . . . .

   Mark 3:13-15 . . . .

4. There are certain basic needs which all believers have. These are areas where the enemy generally attacks. Match the scriptures with the needs and then number them in their order of importance as you see it.

PRIORITY NEEDS

( )   Feeding . . . .

. . . .

( )   Protection . . . .

. . . .

( )   Fellowship . . . .

( )   Assurance of salvation . . . .

( )   Daily Devotional life . . . .

( )   Ability to share testimony . . . .

( )   Ability to share the gospel . . . .

( )   Bible study . . . .

( )   Scripture Memory . . . .

( )   Prayer life . . . .

( )   Growing faith . . . .

SCRIPTURES

Luke 11:1
I Peter 2:2, 3
I John 5:11, 12
Ecc. 4:9, 10

I Peter 5:8
Ps. 5:3
Ps. 107:2

II Tim. 2:15
Job 22:21, 22
Col. 2:6, 7
Rom. 1:16

ASSIGNMENT:

Write the name of one or more people you feel God would have you help in their spiritual walk. Get in touch with them some way this week. What you have already learned in this study booklet gives you a great deal to share in the way of follow-up.

Suggestions For Further Study

Tape BSU 56B — "Indispensable Principles of Training"

Tape 1 — "Born to Reproduce"

New Testament Follow-Up by Wayland B. Moore, Eerdman Publishers

Encouraging New Christians by Michael Griffiths, Inter Varsity Press

Follow-Up by Dawson E. Trotman, The Navigators, Colorado Spring, Colorado

Disciples Are Made—Not Born, by Walter Henrichsen, Victor Press

THE GODLY MAN

AS A

HUSBAND

"The Lord said . . . I will make him a suitable helper, completing him." Gen. 2:18 (Berkeley)

1. What is happening in each picture? . . . .
. . . .

2. How do the pictures relate to each other? . . . .
. . . .

3. What does each picture mean to the wife? . . . .
. . . .

4. What do you feel about each picture? . . . .
. . . .
. . . .
. . . .

Study this picture and be prepared to answer the following questions about it.

1. What does the picture say to you? . . . .
. . . .

2. Guess at the thoughts of each one of the people in the picture.
. . . .
. . . .
. . . .

3. What is really happening? . . . .
. . . .
. . . .

4. Why is it important? . . . .
. . . .
. . . .

Study this picture and be prepared to answer the following
questions about it.

1. What is going on? ....
2. How can you identify with it? ....
   ....
3. Why is it important? ....
   ....

INTRODUCTION TO FAMILY STUDIES

In the world of the Twentieth Century, with its uncertainty, its crumbling value systems and its many social problems and pressures, thinking people are concerned about the home. They are seeking guide lines for effective and fulfilling marriage relationships.

These studies are designed to help improve our understanding of Christian marriage with its challenges, joys, and satisfactions . . . and to produce a distinctively Christian home where Christ lives—not merely a home where Christians live.

The studies leave much unsaid, but this is inevitable within the limits of a single book.

We would highly recommend that you read *Heaven Help the Home* by Howard Hendricks, Victor Press and *How to Be Happy Though Married,* by Dr. Tim LaHaye, Tyndale House, as companion study books for these chapters on marriage, children and the home. These books are on the art and joy of successful family living and cover much of what's been left unsaid in these brief studies. Other helpful tapes and books are listed at the end of each chapter.

CHAPTER XIV

THE BASIS OF MARRIAGE

1. How did God create man? Genesis 1:26, 27

   . . . .
   . . . .
   . . . .

2. Why did God establish the marriage relationship? Genesis
   2:18 . . . .

3. Men and women desire to be married for various reasons. What are some of these motivations?

   MEN   WOMEN

   . . . .
   . . . .
   . . . .
   . . . .
   . . . .

4. In the Bible, God uses marriage to describe the relationship of Christ to the individual believer. What are some
   of the parallels you see between these two relationships?

   . . . .
   . . . .
   . . . .
   . . . .
   . . . .
   . . . .

5. God has given certain scriptural principles which provide
   the basis of a truly Godly marriage. From the following
   Scriptures, state as many of these principles as you can
   find. Genesis 2:18, 24; Eph. 5:21-33; Col. 3:18, 19; I Cor.
   7:3-5; I Cor. 11:3; Genesis 18:19; Genesis 1:26-28.

6. The following are some general principles God has given to Christians. State the principle and how it also contributes to a Godly marriage.

Ephesians 5:18 ....

I Thess. 5:18 ....

Eph. 4:26 ....

Col. 3:23 ....

Eph. 4:31, 32 ....

I Pet. 4:9, Rom. 12:13 ....

Col. 2:6, 7 (Living) ....

Phil. 4:6, 7 ....

Phil. 2:3, 4 ....

Rom. 13:8 ....

II Cor. 6:14 . . . .

7. Which of these principles for a godly marriage is most lacking in your marriage? What can you do this week to begin to change this? . . . .

. . . .

. . . .

. . . .

In order to have a godly marriage, there must be godly partners. The basis of a godly marriage begins with the individual.

8. From the following Scriptures, what are some basic truths that must be evident for God to express His likeness in us? . . . .
   A. John 15:5 . . . .

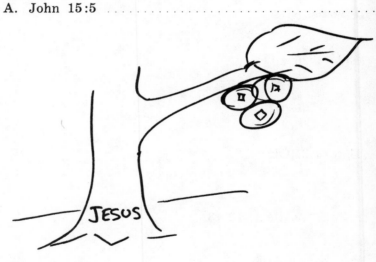

   B. II Cor. 3:18 . . . .
   C. John 3:30 . . . .
   D. II Peter 1:4 . . . .
9. What characteristics relating to godliness do you see in these Scriptures?
   A. Genesis 6:9 . . . .
   B. Heb. 11:8 . . . .
   C. Num. 14:6-8 . . . .
   D. I Kings 4:29 . . . .
   E. Num. 32:12 . . . .

10. In Genesis 18:19 and Ephesians 5:22-24, we found that the husband is to lead the family. In what areas is he to lead?

....

....

Is this true in your family? ....
11. How can a husband who desires to lead his family be kept from it? ....

....

....

....

12. Briefly describe the influence of the men and women in the following verses.
I Peter 3:7 ....
Matt. 27:19-26 ....
I Sam. 25:14-35 ....

....

I Kings 11:1-4 ....

....

I Kings 21:4-16 ....

....

II Kings 4:8-10 ....

....

Esther 4:14-16; 7:3-6; 8:4-8 ....

....

(This reveals how greatly men can influence women, and women can influence men—for good, or for evil.)
13. Who is answerable to God for setting the direction of the home?
A. I Tim. 3:4, 5 ....
B. I Cor. 11:3 ....
C. Col. 3:18-21 ....
14. List the responsibilities of the husband and the wife in the family and home as you understand them.

HUSBAND	WIFE
....	....
....	....
....	....
....	....
....	....

. . . .
. . . .
. . . .
. . . .
. . . .
. . . .
. . . .

15. What if a husband or wife is not fulfilling his/her God-given role—What can the other partner do about it? (I John 3:21, 22; Matt. 21:22; Col. 3:23) . . . .
. . . .

16. In which of these responsibilities do you feel least adequate? . . . .
. . . .

What will you do this week to allow God to help you in this area?
. . . .
. . . .
. . . .
. . . .
. . . .

Suggestions For Further Study

Tape 577 — "The Foundation of The Scriptural Home"
Tape 1059 — "Survey of our Need and God's Provision"
Tape 1057 — "Husband-Wife Relationship"

Building A Christian Home, by Brandt and Dowdy, Victor Books

The Christian Family, by Larry Christenson, Bethany Fellowship.

Do Yourself A Favor, Love Your Wife, by Williams—Logos Press.

CHAPTER XV

THE GODLY MAN
FULFILLING HIS WIFE'S NEEDS
[LOVE]

PART I

Marriage is a trinity — even as God is a trinity. The parts of marriage are the spiritual, emotional and physical. Like a three-legged milk stool — if one part is missing, it becomes ineffective in its operation. Further, the very nature of marriage in its intimacy reveals the weaknesses and short-comings of each partner. With this knowledge comes the ability to hurt deeply. As men, charged before God with the functioning of the home and family, we desperately need to know and understand the needs of our wives and to take the necessary steps to meet them. Only in this way can we adequately fulfill our responsibility and privilege.

I. The wife's emotional needs.

Woman's emotional needs are different than man's. We will consider some of these special needs.

1. How do the following verses apply to the husband/wife relationship?

    A. Eph. 5:25 . . . .

    . . . .

    B. Eph. 5:28-30 . . . .

    . . . .

    . . . .

    . . . .

    . . . .

    C. Col. 3:19 . . . .

    . . . .

    D. I Peter 3:7 . . . .

    . . . .

    E. Eph. 4:31, 32 . . . .

    . . . .

2. Without using reference material, write out your definition of love . . . .

    . . . .

    . . . .

3. Read I Cor. 13 in several translations. Write out the one thing which stands out to you most. . . . .
. . . .
. . . .

4. From verses 1 thru 3, list some things which are good in themselves, but which are worthless without love. What are they? . . . .
. . . .
. . . .
. . . .
. . . .
. . . .

5. True love always expresses itself. The following action **words for love have been taken from several translations of the Bible. Take each one and write out in** your own words: 1) what it means 2) how it works in the home.

   A. Love is patient.
      1). . . . .
      . . . .
      2). . . . .
      . . . .
      . . . .

   B. Love is kind.
      1). . . . .
      . . . .
      2). . . . .
      . . . .

   C. Love is not jealous.
      1). . . . .
      . . . .
      2). . . . .
      . . . .

   D. Love is not boastful.
      1). . . . .
      . . . .
      2). . . . .
      . . . .

E. Love has good manners.

1) ....
....

2) ....
....

F. Love is not selfish.

1) ....
....

2) ....
....

G. Love rejoices in right.

1) ....
....

2) ....
....

H. Love is not arrogant.

1) ....
....

2) ....
....

I. Love is not irritable

1) ....
....

2) ....
....

J. Love is not resentlful

1) ....
....
....
....

2) ....

GUARANTEE
LOVE
NEVER
FAILS

....
....
....

6. What I can do:
From verse 7 of I Cor. 13, select one aspect which seems most important to you. Give an example of how it should work in marriage or in the home and also give an

example of how you will incorporate it in your marriage or home this next week.

A. My choice: ....

....

B. How it should work ....

....

....

C. What I will do ....

....

....

....

Suggestions For Further Study
For Men Only, by J. Allen Peterson, Tyndale
Tape 2777 — "Husband's Responsibility As Lover"
Tape 2773 — "Differences Between Men and Women"
Tape 307 — "Real Love In Marriage"
Tape 1592 — "Christian Marriage"

THE GODLY MAN
FULFILLING HIS WIFE'S NEEDS
[LEADING IN TENDERNESS]

PART II

1. A great emotional need of women is pointed out in Gen. 3:16. What is it? . . . .
. . . .

"Wherever dad sits is the head of the table."

2. What do we discover out of I Cor. 14:8 as to the type of leadership our wives need? . . . .
. . . .
. . . .

"Leadership without love is dictatorship.
Love without leadership is sentimentality."

3. The second most important relationship to any Christian wife is her relationship to her husband. If this is threatened or she doesn't feel secure in it, she becomes resentful, frustrated, hostile and hard to live with. Complete the following thoughts as to some ways we, as husbands, can help our wives continue feeling secure in our love.

   A. By saying daily, "I . . . . you."
   B. By never forgetting special or important . . . .
   C. By expressing appreciation for . . . .

4. Women need to feel like women. Notice the technique in Song of Solomon 2:14, and 4:9. What can you learn from these verses? . . . .
. . . .
. . . .
. . . .

5. Women need to feel wanted and needed. Read Genesis 29:9-20 and write out a list of ways you can make your wife feel wanted today, as Jacob wanted Rachel in those days.

. . . .
. . . .
. . . .
. . . .
. . . .

Women need to be talked to and listened to. One woman said, "You have heard of the great stone face — I married it! His total vocabulary consists of one word, 'uh'. No, there is another word that he uses for emphasis — 'uh huh'." No Marriage fails until communication breaks down.

6. Describe in your own words the ways you think people communicate. . . . .

. . . .

. . . .

. . . .

7. What are some important reasons for keeping each other adequately informed?

. . . .

. . . .

. . . .

. . . .

8. What does Amos 3:3 teach us about communications? . . . .

. . . .

9. COMMUNICATION AIDS. Under each verse below list: 1) The basic principle described in this verse, 2) the opposite of this principle, and 3) the problems in communication caused by not following this principle.

   A. Eph. 4:15
      1) . . . .

      . . . .

      2) . . . .

      . . . .

      3) . . . .

      . . . .

   B. Eph. 4:25-27
      1) . . . .

      . . . .

      2) . . . .

      . . . .

      3) . . . .

      . . . .

C. Eph. 4:29

    1) ....

    ....

    2) ....

    ....

    3) ....

D. Prov. 15:1

    1) ....

    ....

    2) ....

    ....

    3) ....

E. Prov. 18:13

    1) ....

    ....

    2) ....

    ....

    3) ....

F. James 1:19

    1) ....

    ....

    2) ....

    3) ....

10. Match the verses with the problems or barriers to communication in a marriage.

PROBLEMS OR BARRIERS	SCRIPTURES
_____	Luke 6:31
_____	Prov. 13:10
_____	Eph. 4:31
_____	Eph. 4:26
_____	Phil. 2:3,4
_____	Prov. 10:8
_____	Esther 4:11
_____	John 3:19,20
_____	Is. 53:6
_____	Jeremiah 17:9

11. Where do you fall short in communication? What one thing will you do this week to improve the situation? Share your application with a friend and ask him to check up on you to see how it went.

. . . .
. . . .
. . . .
. . . .
. . . .
. . . .

Suggestions For Further Study

Tape 1062 — "Communication Between Husband and Wife"
Tape 2776 — "Husband's Responsibility As Leader"
Tape 2775 — "Communication Between Husband and Wife"
Tape 1153 — "The Home"
Tape 2317 — "The Spirit Filled Home"

THE GODLY MAN
FULFILLING HIS WIFE'S NEEDS
[BEING HER HERO]

PART III

1. Women need consideration, tenderness and understanding.
Name the principles found in the following verses and passages regarding these things:

A. Eph. 4:2 ....
....

B. Psalms 18:35 ....
....

C. I Peter 5:5,6 ....
....

D. Luke 10:30-36 ....
....

E. II Sam. 9:1-10 ....
....

F. Genesis 33:12-14 ....
....

2. A wife needs to be proud of her husband:
A. Appearance: I Sam. 16:7
   1) Who does look on the outward appear-
      ance? ....
      ....
      ....
   2) What does God Look on?.....................
      ....
   3) How does I Cor. 9:22 apply to our appearance?
      ....
      ....
   4) What should be the motive of our hearts in caring for
      our appearance?
      a. Matt. 5:16 ....
         ....
      b. Luke 16:10 ....
         ....
         ....

—107—

B. Integrity.
　　1) Define integrity in your own words. . . . .
　　. . . . .
　　. . . . .
　　. . . . .
　　2) What truths about integrity can be discovered from
　　　the following verses?
　　　a. Job 2:3 . . . .
　　　. . . . .
　　　b. Ps. 7:8 . . . .
　　　. . . . .
　　　c. Ps. 25:21 . . . .
　　　. . . . .
　　　d. Ps. 41:12 . . . .
　　　. . . . .
　　　e. Prov. 11:3 . . . .
　　　. . . . .
　　　f. Prov. 20:7 . . . .
　　　. . . . .

C. Consistency and faithfulness.
　　1) What do we learn about our God from Mal. 3:6 and
　　　Heb. 13:8? . . . .
　　　. . . . .
　　　. . . . .
　　2) How does this apply to us in our marriage relation-
　　　ship? . . . .
　　　. . . . .
　　　. . . . .
　　3) What does James 1:8 warn against? . . . .
　　　. . . . .
　　4) Why was Hananiah given charge over Jerusalem in
　　　Nehemiah 7:2? . . . .
　　　. . . . .
　　5) Why, in Psalm 12:1, was David calling upon God for
　　　help? . . . .
　　　. . . . .
　　6) From Prov. 20:6, what do we learn about the avail-
　　　ability of faithful men? . . . .
　　　. . . . .
　　　. . . . .

7) Why did his enemies have difficulty in finding fault with Daniel? Dan. 6:4 ....

....

8) What kind of a servant did Jesus commend in Matt. 25:21? ....

....

9) What can we discover about faithfulness from Luke 16:10-12? ....

....

....

....

10) Integrity, consistency and faithfulness always find positive expression in the life. Read Psalm 15 in several translations and list the things you find there which are marks of a godly man.

....

....

....

....

....

....

11) Review your answers to this chapter and ask God to reveal to you which one of these areas is the weakest in your own life. Write it down.

....

....

Now, what will you do this next week to help correct this fault? ....

....

....

....

....

....

Suggestions Fro Further Study

Tape 1154 — "Role and Responsibility of the Husband"
Tape 1547 — "What Kind of a Partner Are You?"
Tape 779 — "Marks of a Man of God"
Tape 1866 — "Marks of a Committed Christian—Part I"
Tape 1888 — "Marks of a Committed Christian—Part II"

THE GODLY MAN
FULFILLING HIS WIFE'S NEEDS
[PHYSICAL]

PART IV

1. What does I Tim. 5:8 mean to you? . . . .

. . . .

. . . .

2. What does Eph. 5:31 mean to you regarding the marriage relationship? . . . .

. . . .

. . . .

The sexual part of marriage is perhaps the least spoken to, and yet one of the most important. The Bible gives some clear directions which we will do well to heed.

3. What command was given in Genesis 1:27,28 before sin ever entered the world? . . . .

. . . .

4. What did God, in His infinite wisdom, declare in Genesis 2:18? . . . .

. . . .

Marriage and sex are of divine origin. Grace perfects them. Sin perverts them.

5. From the following verses, list some reasons you believe God instituted sex and marriage? . . . .

Psalm 127:3-5 . . . .

I Cor. 7:2-5 . . . .

Gen. 2:24 . . . .

16. Write out in your own words the meaning of I Cor. 7:2-5 and then write how this should operate in marriage.

. . . .

. . . .

. . . .

. . . .

. . . .

. . . .

. . . .

. . . .

The sex act to a man is mainly physical. To a woman it is not only physical but emotional and spiritual. It is the closest thing to totally giving herself that a woman can express in an act. This being true, a woman will not and cannot function well sexually while torn up emotionally. A satisfactory sexual relationship is mainly a husband's project A sexual conflict may exist between husband and wife if there is a feeling of competition, resentment carried over from courtship, too large an age difference or differing sexual drives. The husband may have personal

problems of feeling inadequate sexually, or being domineering and selfish. The wife's problem may spring from inner fears, pain in the relationship, puritanical ideas, or feelings of guilt and being used instead of loved. Sexual conflict may also be caused by a physical health problem in either party, a lack of time (too much to do) or simply tiredness. The first step in solving any problem is determining the cause.

7. How would you counsel a man who came to you with the following problems?

   A. I have a greater sexual drive than my wife. She acts like she is doing me a favor when we have relationships. . . . . . .

   . . . .

   . . . .

   B. I get satisfied more quickly than my wife and this seems to leave her frustrated. . . . .

   . . . .

   . . . .

   C. After we have relations, my wife always wants to talk and I want to go to sleep. . . . .

   . . . .

   . . . .

   D. It seems like my wife's sexual desires have been dwindling steadily since the first couple of years of our marriage. . . .

   . . . .

   . . . .

   . . . .

E. Many times as we dress for bed, I indicate a sexual interest to my wife, but she seems to have little interest at that time. . . . .
. . . .
. . . .

F. By the time my work day is over, I often find myself too tired to enjoy sexual relationships. . . . .
. . . .
. . . .

G. It seems like my wife is always too tired to really enjoy our sharing love together. . . . .
. . . .

H. My sexual satisfaction is dependent on my wife being satisfied. Yet, she has a hard time reaching fulfillment. . . .
. . . .
. . . .
. . . .

Comment: Remembering five words will help any man improve or maintain the sexual aspect of his marriage. Don't be: hurried, crude, rude, impatient, or selfish.

ASSIGNMENT: Many sexual problems in marriage are caused by lack of communication on the part of one partner or the other as to personal likes and dislikes regarding the sex act. **Pray for boldness to openly discuss this with your wife** so that both of you may experience an ever-increasing joy in each other as God intends.

Suggestions For Further Study
Tape 1154 — "Marriage and God's Purpose For Sex"
Tape 1863 — "The Other Side of Sex"
Sexual Happiness In Marriage, by H. J. Miles, Zondervan
How to be Happy Though Married, by Dr. Tim LaHaye, Tyndale House
(Two very excellent tapes on the sexual relationship in marriage are also available from the free lending library of Dr. Ed Wheat, Springdale, Arkansas.)

CHAPTER XVI

USING THE HOME AS
A PLACE OF MINISTRY

A Christian home is a mighty tool in the hands of God to convince a lost and dying world of the reality of Jesus Christ. The warm atmosphere of such a home is often the climate neces-

sary to bring a skeptical unbeliever to the point of considering the claims of Christ. Having friends in for coffee or for a meal, starting a neighborhood Bible discussion group, making the home available for prayer groups, and allowing God to express Himself to others through hospitality, are some ways a home can be used.

1. Home is a place to which people come or from which people go.
   A. Which of these is more important? . . . .
   Why? . . . . :
   . . . .
   . . . .
   . . . .

   B. How would you define hospitality? Titus 1:8, Romans 12:13 . . . .
   . . . .

   C. What is the significance of giving a person a meal? See Luke 19:5-10, Luke 24:28-31 . . . .
   . . . .

2. In the story recorded in Luke 10:29-37, how would you describe a neighbor? . . . .
   . . . .

3. What was the governing power behind Paul's ministry? II Cor. 5:14, 15 . . . .

4. What is the purpose of ministering to others? Eph. 4: 11-16, Col. 1:28, 29 . . . .
   . . . .

5. Note the following examples of hospitality. Write down (a) who gave the hospitality (b) who received it, and (c) what blessings the ones who gave the hospitality received as a result of it. (You may have to read further in the assigned portions to discern this.)

Gen. 18:1-8

A.

B.

C.

Gen. 24:17-20

A.

B.

C.

Joshua 2:1-16

A.

B.

C.

I Kings 17:10-24

A.

B.

C.

II Kings 4:8-11

A.

B.

C.

Luke 10:38-42

A.

B.

C.

Acts 16:14, 15

A.

B.

C.

6. To whom should we offer hospitality?

A. Leviticus 19:33, 34

B. Isaiah 58:7

C. Matt. 25:34-46

D. I Peter 4:9

E. III John 5-8 . . . .

7. What are some of the reasons we should show hospitality?
A. Isaiah 60:11 . . . .
B. Eccl. 11:1 . . . .
C. Heb. 13:1, 2 . . . .
8. To whom are we not to extend hospitality? II John 10-11

9. Who is the most hospitable couple you know? . . . .

Write out the outstanding characteristics, as you see them,
which make them hospitable. . . . .

ASSIGNMENT:
Real hospitality is costly in time, privacy, involvement, and
money. Do you think the investment is worth it? . . . .
If so, discuss with your partner how your home can be used to
minister to others more effectively. Write out a plan and
schedule as to how and when your home will become a more
available tool in the hands of God for the blessing of others.

Suggestions For Further Study
Tape 1021 — "Use of the Home in the Ministry"
Tape 1279 — "Hospitality"

THE GODLY MAN

AS A

FATHER

Study this picture and be prepared to answer the following
questions about it.

1. Why are the children in such shape? . . . .
. . . .

2. Where are their parents? . . . .

3. What are the children thinking? . . . .
. . . .

4. What future do you feel they have? . . . .
. . . .

5. How do you feel about the picture? . . . .
. . . .
. . . .

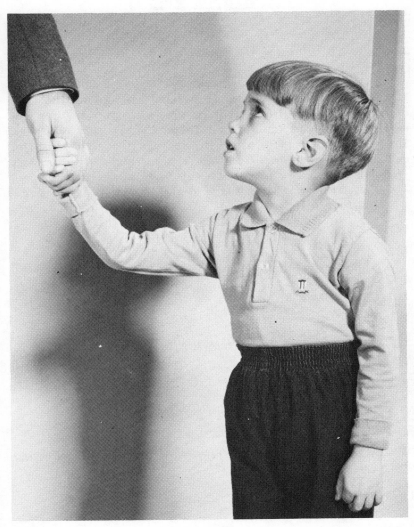

Study this picture and be prepared to answer the following question about it.

1.   What does the picture say to you? . . . .
. . . .
. . . .
. . . .
. . . .

CHAPTER XVII

RESPONSIBILITIES
TO OUR CHILDREN

"Your children are God's assignment or commission, and He does not waste children on parents. He knows the very kind to send you. Did you think God gave you children because of what you could do for them? That's only one part. He gave them because of what they could do for you. You can meet your children's particular needs and they can meet yours in a unique and special way."—Howard Hendricks

1. What are the various words used in Psalm 127 to describe children? ....
   ....
   ....
   What do each of these words mean to you? ....
   ....
   ....
   ....

2. Who is responsible for training the children?
   A. Proverbs 1:8 ....
   B. Proverbs 29:15-17
   ....
   What is the mother's responsibility? ....
   ....
   ....

3. What are the parents' responsibilities in the following verses:
   A. Eph. 6:4 ....
   B. Deut. 6:4-7
   C. Prov. 2:1, 3:1, 4:1, 5:1, 7:1 ....
   ....
   ....
   ....
   ....

4. How are we to love our children?
   A. Matt. 3:17 ....
   B. Gen. 22:2 ....

C. II Sam. 18:33 ....

D. Luke 8:40-42 & 49-56 ....

E. I Cor. 13:4-7 ....

....

5. Define the following terms:

A. Teach ....

....

B. Instruct ....

....

C. Train ....

....

D. Discipline ....

....

E. Nurture ....

....

6. What does Psalm 127:3 teach us concerning our responsibility? ....

....

7. What are children like?

A. I Cor. 14:20 ....

B. I Cor. 3:1-3 ....

C. Mark 10:15 ....

8. A lack of security plagues the younger generation today. They are grasping for something stable, unmoveable, and real. From the following Scriptures, list some things we can do as a parent to help our children be secure:

A. Prov. 22:6 ....

....

B. Prov. 14:26 (Living) ....

C. II Cor. 1:17-19 (Living) ....

....

D. Matt. 18:10-14 ....

....

E. Prov. 3:11, 12 ....

....

9. What is the learning process?
   A. James 1:2-4 ....
   B. II Peter 1:12-15 ....
Note the spiral of learning: repetition, experience, relearning, experience and so forth. This should produce progressive change upward toward more complete understanding.
10. Where else do children learn apart from the home?
    A. Prov. 1:10-14 ....
    B. Ps. 119:105 ....
    C. John 14:26 ....
    D. I Sam. 12:23
11. Read Hebrews 12:5-11 in at least three translations. Then record what, to you, are the four most important aspects of this passage.
    A. ....
    B. ....
    C. ....
    D. ....
12. Match the following Scriptures with the principles involved regarding discipline:

PRINCIPLES		SCRIPTURES
Expression of love	....	Matt. 5:37
Don't nag	....	Prov. 13:24
Be consistent	....	Eccl. 5:5
Be fair	....	Gen. 37:3
Be impartial	....	James 1:8
Use an inanimate object	....	Acts 10:34
Fulfill every promise	....	Prov. 23:13, 14
Don't lose your temper	....	Prov. 25:28
Get the facts	....	Prov. 18:13
Do it now	....	Eccl. 8:11

13. What can be the result of undisciplined children?
    A. I Sam. 3:13 ....
    B. Titus 1:16, I Tim. 3:4 ....
    ....
    C. Prov. 29:15 ....
    ....
    D. Prov. 19:18 (Living) "Discipline your son in his early years while there is hope. If you don't you will ruin his life." ....
    ....
    ....

Proper discipline is a crying need of every child.

14. What are some of the reasons fathers do not discipline their children? . . . .

. . . .

. . . .

. . . .

. . . .

. . . .

15. Children also need encouragement. Match the ways of encouragement with the following Scriptures:

WAYS		SCRIPTURES
Be kind and understanding	. . . .	James 1:19
Listen to them	. . . .	Prov. 31:26
Take time for them	. . . .	Eccl. 3:1
Take time with them	. . . .	John 21:3-6
Be interested in their interests	. . . .	Mark 3:14
Show your love and approval	. . . .	1 Jn. 3:18

16. In what ways have your children been a spiritual blessing to you? . . . .

. . . .

. . . .

. . . .

17. From the following examples from the Word of God, what would you say is one of the greatest influences in forming a child's character? John 4:53, Job 1:5, Mark 5:22-24, 41, 42 . . . .

. . . .

. . . .

. . . .

18. Write in these columns what you feel your strengths and weaknesses are as a parent.

STRENGTHS	WEAKNESSES
. . . .	. . . .
. . . .	. . . .
. . . .	. . . .
. . . .	. . . .
. . . .	. . . .
. . . .	. . . .
. . . .	. . . .

PRACTICAL HELPS

A. Life of the parents

1) We can't make Christ a reality to them if He is not to us. II Tim. 1:5
2) Practice what you want them to practice. I Cor. 11:1
   a. Disciples are followers. Children follow and imitate us; we're making disciples after our own pattern of living. Phil. 4:9
   b. If we want them to have our characteristics, have them around. Mark 3:14a
3) Pray for wisdom. James 1:5
4) Mom and Dad TOGETHER in discipline. Ps. 133:1
5) Encourage and support one another regarding the children. Deut. 3:28a
6) Don't be touchy or over-protective regarding the children. Prov. 28:25a
7) Prayer—keep the children committed. I Sam. 1:27, 28
8) Watch parental pride. It is easy to require too much when we want to make an impression. Phil. 2:3, 4

B. Encouragement

1) Be tolerant and understanding. Prov. 31:26
2) Be a good listener. Give your undivided attention. James 1:19
3) Take time for them. Your presence means everything. Eccl. 3:1
4) Plan family activities. .
5) Consider them in family decisions.
6) Be interested in their interests. Illus. John 21:3-6
7) Be vocal in expressions of love. Let them know you love them and look for ways to show love. I Jn. 3:18

C. Discipline or training

1) Discipline only in the principles. (i.e. disobedience, dishonesty, disrespect, untruthfulness, etc.) Prov. 29:17
2) Discipline FIRMLY but NOT in temper. Col. 3:21
3) Set realistic standards and requirements. Amos 7:7

a. Not too high. Don't expect too much; it results in trouble. Superimposed spirituality now means carnality later. Matt. 15:8
b. Plan to keep them. Prov. 13:19
c. Let children know what is expected. Be sure it is clear. Prov. 22:6
d. Be consistent. James 1:6
e. Avoid "if you do that again" syndrome.
f. Don't expose them to public ridicule.
g. Don't indulge them.
h. Be willing to apologize when needed.
i. Don't nag.
5) Get children to help. I Sam. 16:11
6) The greatest thing parents can do for their children is to love one another.

Suggestions For Further Study

Tape 1150AB — "Child Rearing I"
Tape 1151AB — "Child Rearing II"
Tape 1152AB — "Child Rearing III"
Tape 971A — "Disciplining"
Tape 971B — "Restricting"
Tape 26 — "Parent-Child Relationship"
Tape 1064 — "Spiritual Goals for the Child"
Tape 1065 — "The Child's Two Needs; Love & Discipline"
Tape 1807 & 1808 — "Priesthood of Parents"
Tape 1811 & 1812 — "God's Order for Parents"
Tape 1965 — "God's Order for Children"
Parents on the Run by Willard & Marguerite Beecher, Julian Press
Dare to Discipline by James Dobson, Tyndale House
Children, Fun or Frenzy by Mr. and Mrs. Al Fabrizio, Box 182, Palo Alto, California
Heaven Help the Home, by Howard Hendricks, Victor Press
Understanding Your Children, by Dr. Clyde Narramore, Zondervan publishers.